The Fea:

CU00588500

Sometimes the Only Thing Standing Between
You and Success is... You!

Richard Fenton & Andrea Waltz

ISBN 978-0-9774393-5-5

You are invited to visit the authors at

www.CourageCrafters.com

(800) 290-5028

This book is dedicated to people of courage everywhere who have looked fear in the eye and said with a smile,

"This is my life. You can't have it."

Please Note:

The information and ideas contained in this book are intended to act as inspiration and motivation, <u>not</u> as a substitute for competent medical or mental health intervention when it is required.

-The Publisher & Authors

Note from the Authors

Perhaps the most profound discovery of the 20th century is the fact that we become what we think about most. But what if what you think about most are your fears? What will your legacy be then? Who wants their legacy to be that of a fear-filled person?

The problem, of course, is that it is almost impossible not to think about one's fears. It's a dilemma for which there is only one rational approach; to allow yourself to think about your fears... but to think differently.

Fear is by far the most powerful and destructive of all emotions, forcing you inside yourself. It paralyzes you, makes you flee when you should take a stand. But the worst thing about fear is that it cheats people from achieving the greatest gift of all... the ability to experience life to its fullest.

In our book and personal development program called Go for No!, we make the case that increasing your failure rate — learning to embrace failure as a tool and to enjoy hearing the word no — can propel you forward and accelerate your progress toward success. This program, on the other hand, makes the case for developing the ability to say no... not to other people (though that can be a valuable skill, too) but, rather, to your fears.

Now, you may be wondering: what makes us qualified to talk about fear? Admittedly, neither of us have Ph.D.'s in psychology, so it's a fair question. Be assured, we have plenty of experience dealing with fear; more than you'll ever know, and more than we'll ever fully admit!

3

As a result we have invested substantial time and resources contemplating and studying what we believe to be the single most destructive force in the world - so that it would no longer be the most destructive force it is.

You may also be wondering if our studies and introspections have made us fearless. The answer is; no. We have come to accept that we will never be totally fearless. You will never be fully fearless, either.

Nor should you want to be! Because no one is ever completely fearless, and those who claim they are, are either lying or not living to their potential by avoiding things that scare and challenge them!

But we do know two things:

Sometimes the only thing standing between you and success is you

We'd rather be locked in an actual prison than be confined to the virtual prison of our fears. At least with a brick and mortar prison there is the chance of escape; but from the prison of one's fears there is no escape. Unless… of course… you have the key.

Will the Fear Factory be the key that unlocks the prison door in your mind? We certainly hope so.

.

Richard Fenton   Andrea Waltz

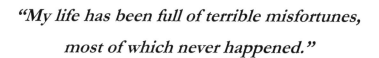

"My life has been full of terrible misfortunes, most of which never happened."

-The French Philosopher Montaigne

Chapter One: Steven

It was a sunny Seattle morning, a rarity in a land that isn't known for sun. I knotted the new yellow power tie I had picked up at Macy's the day before, slipped on my Hickey-Freeman suit, and made the short walk from my two-bedroom condo near the waterfront to the Pike Street Market, a well-known Seattle tourist attraction made even more famous by the *FISH!* training program that teaches people to C-Y-A... *choose your attitude*. I had personally taken the CYA approach to business and life long before fish became the topic du jour. Of course, in the past, the acronym had stood for something else entirely.

Now, there's something about Seattle that has always felt right to me. It's difficult to explain, but the chilly, misty morning air matches my personality somehow, not that I am a 'chilly' person. To the contrary, people who know me would describe me as warm and friendly. But in my position as an account executive for Ramsden+Media, a boutique ad agency known for cutting-edge ideas and attention to its customers, I have come to discover that warm and friendly is not always enough.

Indeed, to be successful in the highly competitive world of advertising one must also be smart and creative, intense and focused, and have the fearless killer instinct of a bull-shark.

I am some of these. But when it really comes down to it, I am more pike than shark.

To be successful in the ad game, like most of life, you need to embrace challenges and be adaptable to change. But, for a person who makes his living in a world that thrives on change, my world is admittedly routine. I wake in the same bed 350 days a year. To make coordinating my wardrobe easier, I wear the same color suit (navy), the same color shirt (white), and the same color necktie (pale blue), although I do try to mix up the patterns a bit. And, barring the occasional breakfast meeting with an account, I have the same triple-shot, grandé non-fat cappuccino, and the same pecan-crusted bran muffin, at the same little café in the market every morning.

And I admit I like it that way.

But, today, as I enter the café, something seems askew. I can't quite put my finger on it, but I have the same feeling I assume an animal has just before an earthquake – kind of a low-grade sense of something big lurking just over the horizon. I try to put the thought out of my mind, popping a good-sized bite of bran muffin in my mouth just as my cell phone rings. Isn't that always the case?! And, looking down, I see the name Yvonne on the screen.

Chapter Two: Yvonne

That low-grade feeling that started at the café was still present as I entered Yvonne Ramsden's large, glass enclosed office on the third floor of the building that housed virtually all aspects of the business, including creative, art, and sales.

As usual, even with a regular telephone on her desk within reach, Yvonne had her cell phone pressed to her ear. As Yvonne explained to me once, the day was coming when all communication would be done via cell phone, and land lines would be totally obsolete. She was just getting ahead of the curve!

Glancing up, she motioned for me to take a seat and I plopped myself down in one of two large, red leather chairs. Yvonne loved red. She also loved how people would literally melt into the intentionally-overly-soft cushions, allowing her to tower over them. Any advantage is a good advantage, she always said.

She clicked off and I struggled in vain to sit upright.

"Steven, you look positively… the same as you always look," she began, eyeing my outfit. "You should think about getting a new tie. Red would be nice."

"This is a new tie," I stated flatly. "And, besides, red is your color, Yvonne. I wouldn't want to encroach." Apparently the small talk was over as Yvonne hit me with the big question:

"Fearn International, what do you know about them?"

Fearn International? That caught me off-guard. What I knew about Fearn was what everyone knew. Based in Portland, Oregon, Fearn International was a manufacturer of everything under the sun - auto parts, home furnishings, sporting goods, and kitchen sinks... literally. And with sales in the neighborhood of $30 Billion and profits too obscene to utter aloud, Fearn made Microsoft look like a child in corporate diapers. Why was she asking? I wondered, my throat going suddenly dry.

"They're a monster," I managed.

"Well, the monster is scratching at the door," Yvonne stated.

"But they don't advertise!" I protested. "Never have and never will."

Fearn was what people referred to as a 'stealth' company, meaning they manufactured private-label goods behind the scenes for other companies, who then put their names on the products. As such, Fearn had vowed to keep a low profile and had always operated under the public radar.

"Never say never, Steven," Yvonne said as she slid a sheet of cream colored stationary across the desk in my direction.

As I scanned the document, my heart began to race: Fearn had decided to launch a line of products under their own name and was inviting six of the nation's top ad agencies to compete for the business, the dollar amount of which was underlined in the final sentence of the letter. It was a number which needed no underlining.

"One week from today Ramsden+Media will be pitching - let me restate that, Steven; *you* will be pitching our services to thirty Fearn International top executives at their corporate headquarters."

"Thirty people?" I managed, trying to hide my sudden discomfort. "Sounds more like a speech than a pitch."

"You're right, Steven, that's exactly what it is – a speech! And it has to be magnificent, your best effort. Glowing… radiant… it has to be…."

"Perfect?"

"Yes! It has to be perfect! Are you up to being perfect, Steven?"

"Perfect is my middle name," I replied, putting on my best face.

"That's what I wanted to hear!" Yvonne said with a smile. "Now, there is one other thing…" Isn't there always? I thought, waiting for the other shoe to drop.

"I'm assigning Doug Appleton to assist," Yvonne continued. "He'll be going with you on the pitch." This was not the other shoe I expected. I felt like a child that had been given a helium balloon, only to have one of Yvonne's red finger nails reach out and pop it.

Yvonne glared at me through emerald green eyes, unflinching, waiting for my response.

"I understand why you'd assign someone to assist, but why Doug?"

Of course, I knew why. Though I was the senior guy, Doug Appleton was an up-and-comer, what people referred to as a 'go-to' guy; rock steady, self-assured, bordering on cocky, a salesman's-salesman with ice water running through his veins where most mortals simply had blood. Truth be told, after what had happened at the InterTech presentation the month before, I should have been pleased that Yvonne didn't tap Doug to present and *me* to assist.

"Doug doesn't have half your creativity, Steven, but he's unflappable," Yvonne said flatly.

Unflappable?

Her words stung more than I wanted to show, because – whether it was said or not – the underlying implication was that I was somehow *flappable*.

"So, you want this or not, Steven? I mean, if this is beyond you capabilities…"

"Of course I want it!" I said, cutting her off and jumping to my feet.

Yvonne gave me a squinting smile, picked up her cell phone and started dialing, a clear signal that two things had just been decided: One, the meeting was over, and, two, Doug Appleton and I would be joined at the hip for the next two weeks.

Chapter Three: Doug

I could have flown to Portland but opted instead to make the 175 mile drive, in part for the solitude it afforded; in part so I could take advantage of the time to practice my presentation; but mostly because one of my many fears is flying. No, that's not technically correct. No one is actually afraid of flying - it's crashing we're afraid of. The flying part is just fine!

As I expected, the sunny skies that started the day gave way to what is lovingly referred to by those who make their home in the Pacific Northwest as 'showers', the preferred term over what it really was... *rain!*

Guiding my company-issued Lexus into the underground parking lot at the Fearn International headquarters, I glanced at the dashboard clock which read 9:45 a.m. - plenty of time to park, buy a bottle of water and make my way to the 14th floor.

I grabbed my PowerPoint projector and entered the lobby where I found Doug Appleton leaning against a wall and working his mouth with a tooth pick like a miner digging for gold.

"Morning, Doug."

"Cutting it kind of close, don't you think, buddy boy?" Doug said, glancing at his watch. I reached past him and pushed the "up" button without responding. But Doug wasn't done trying to get under my skin.

"You don't like me much, do you, Stevie?"

"Never thought about it one way or the other, Doug," I lied.

"You ever wonder why Yvonne assigned me to assist on this pitch?" Doug asked. The word 'unflappable' came to mind, but instead I said: "No, but I'm sure you're going to tell me."

"It's simple. I'm your *just in case* guy," Doug said.

"My *just in case* guy?" I repeated, squinting at him as if I didn't know what he meant. But I knew exactly what he meant.

"You know… just in case something happens," Doug said. "In case things don't go exactly as planned. Like, let's say you suddenly felt dizzy and…" The guy was pushing it now. "Listen, Doug," I said through gritted teeth, "it was a mild hypo-glycemic reaction caused by low blood sugar. It wasn't that big a deal."

"Hypo-glycemic reaction? Get real, Steve. You had a full-blown panic attack and passed out in the middle of a client pitch and everyone knows it.

I mean, you went down like a featherweight with a glass jaw who got clobbered with an uppercut from Muhammad Ali!"

The anger started to rise inside me like steam. I tugged on my shirt collar to release some of the heat as the elevator doors slid open, my mouth starting to go dry. I wish I'd remembered to buy water.

"Well, if you *do* go down for the count again," Doug said with a chuckle as we stepped into the empty elevator, "don't sweat it, because Doug's here to save your bacon." The silence was deafening as we climbed toward the 14th floor,

Doug looking straight ahead with a smug little smile painted on his lips, me clutching my projector case like a life raft. I glanced at my watch which read 9:54 a.m. and tried to calm myself, turning my mental focus to the looming presentation. That's when I realized that what Doug was hinting at was true - I truly had no business making this presentation.

"Doug, I've been thinking," I started, angry at myself for what I was about to say. "But maybe you should make the presentation." Oh, my God, did I just actually ask Doug to do the presentation?

"Good call, Steven! After all, a man's got to know his limits," Doug said, reaching out and taking the projector case from my sweaty hand.

"You don't even have to come in the boardroom; you can just hang out in the hall."

Yes, I had.

And, just then - as the elevator slowed to a stop - I suddenly began to feel light-headed. I leaned against the wall as a precaution, just in case I lost it. Then I thought: You've got to fight this feeling off. You've got to do this presentation. You've got to do this! This is one of those defining moments where your destiny is defined. I had no idea how prophetic that thought would turn out to be.

Chapter Four: Sturgess

The elevator doors began to slide open and suddenly we were thrown into pitch blackness. For a brief moment I thought maybe I had had another panic attack and simply passed out.

"Looks like a power outage," I said to Doug, but there was no response.

"Doug? Are you there?" No reply.

"This is no time for games, Appleton," I said firmly. "Where are you?" Still no response.

I knew I couldn't stand there in the elevator forever. As scared as I was to step out of the elevator into the darkness of the hallway, I was more frightened to stay in the elevator. What if the doors slid closed and trapped me inside? What if the elevator car started to fall?! Need I mention that I have a fear of falling?

Feeling my way along the wall I made my way out of the elevator and stepped into the hallway. I held up my hand and wiggled my fingers and literally could not see my hand in front of my face.

"Hello! Is anyone there?" I called out. Why haven't the emergency generators kicked on? I wondered.

I continued groping the wall with my outstretched arm, my heart racing, until I finally located a door. I searched for the knob, turned it, and was surprised when light flooded from the room like water bursting from a broken dam. Apparently the electricity wasn't out in the entire building.

I stumbled into the room with a gasp, relief washing over me. I had never thought of myself as someone who was afraid of the dark, but clearly I needed to add this to my list of fears.

Pulling myself together I looked up, fully expecting to see a receptionist sitting at a desk with the gold and blue Fearn International logo looming overhead - but, no.
Sitting at a computer in the center of the room was a curious little man who looked somewhat like a troll from Lord of the Rings. I noticed that the walls contained no art whatsoever. In fact - with the exception of a single, fire-engine red door on the far side of the room - everything in the office was either black or white.

"Get in here and shut that door!" the curious little man yelled.

"What? I just…"

"Are you hearing impaired?" the man shouted. "I said, close the door!"

I stepped into the room and quickly closed the door behind me.

"Excuse me, but there's a power outage of some sort and..."

"There's no power outage," the man stated. "You came in through the dark room, is all. It happens all the time."

"The dark room?" I asked.

"Yes, the dark room, where fears are developed. It's a play on words; dark room... where fears are developed... clever, huh? Came up with that one myself." I had no idea what the little man was talking about, and quite frankly, I didn't care.

"I'm looking for the headquarters of Fearn International. I've got an important presentation to make in just a few minutes."

"Don't worry about it," he said. "There's no time here, so your meeting will wait."

"I'm sorry. What did you say?"

"You *are* hearing impaired, aren't you?" he declared. "I said: There's... no... time... here!" As amusing as this little man was, I could no longer tolerate his mad ramblings.

"I don't have time for this. I'm late for a meeting!" I repeated.

"Don't believe me?" he said. "Go ahead, check your watch."

I glanced down at my watch to discover it was stopped at 9:54 a.m., the second hand frozen like an icicle.

"So, while I've got you here, and – since there's no rush to be anywhere since there is no time to worry about – let me try this new fear out on you! Come. Sit!" he said, lifting his aging frame from the chair and patting the seat of the chair with his hand.

"But…"

He patted the chair again, smiling a crooked smile. "It will just take a minute, and, besides…"

"… there's no time here, I get it." I said, finishing his sentence. I lowered myself in the chair and followed the crooked finger that pointed at the computer screen.

"Imagine you just bought a new computer and you were working on a file that you wanted to save," the little man said. "What would you do?"

"Simple. I'd do this," I said, using the mouse to click on 'file' and then on 'save'. I figured the quicker I did what he wanted, the quicker I'd get out of here.

"Excellent!" he said gleefully. "Now, try typing something." I tapped several letters on the keyboard and saw immediately that the screen was frozen.

"Frozen like a turkey, two weeks before thanksgiving!" the little man declared with delight. "Enough to scare anyone to not want to buy a computer, don't you think?"

Without a word I reached out and simultaneously pressed the control/alt/delete keys on the keyboard, rebooted the computer and recovered the file. The little man's smile quickly evaporated and his wrinkled, troll-like-face scrunched up with displeasure.

"That's the problem with computer fears!" he declared, his voice filled with disdain. "They work great on old farts like me, but not the young ones like you. And it's damn near impossible to create a computer fear that fazes a ten year old. Oh, well, back to the drawing board."

"Who are you?" I asked.

The little man reached into his pocket, pulled out a business card and held it out in his withered hand. It read: *Miles Sturgess, Head Programmer, Cyberphobia Division.*

"Cyberphobia is a relatively new division," he began. "I first wanted to launch it in the 1950's, but they said it was too early – only a handful of people even knew what a computer was back then, so there was no use creating a fear that has a market potential of less than 1% of the population! So they waited until the late-seventies when Jobs and Wozniak started the Apple thing - probably a smart move."

"You keep saying, *they*. Who are they?"

"They are they. You know… *them!*"

This guy was starting to seriously bug me. "No, I don't know. *Them, who?*"

Sturgess stepped closer, leaned in and said in a whisper: *"The Fear Masters."*

Chapter Five: The Fear Factory

The Fear Masters I repeated quietly, as if I had just been let in on the world's best-kept secret. Sturgess sat quietly, waiting for the next question which he must have known was sure to come.

"What is this place?" I croaked.

"Ah! This, my dear boy," Sturgess said with a sweep of his hand, "is the place where fears are manufactured and distributed. This… is… *The Fear Factory!*"

"That's ridiculous!" I blurted. "There's no such thing as a fear factory," suddenly realizing this whole thing was some kind of elaborate joke. "Okay, Doug, the joke's over," I shouted. "You can come out now!"

"Doug's not here, Steven," said Sturgess with a serious face. "And, I assure you, this is no joke."

"How did you know my name?" I said incredulously, realizing I had never introduced myself.

"And you think the idea of a fear factory is ridiculous?" Sturgess continued, ignoring my question. "Where, exactly, do you think fears come from?"

"Well, I… I don't know," I stammered. "I guess I thought we're born with them, that fears are already in people."

"Like a standard option on your car?" Sturgess asked with a laugh.

"Yeah, something like that. Like cruise control."

"Well, let me set you straight, my young friend. There are only three fears that come standard when you're born: *the fear of falling... the fear of loud noises... and the fear of abandonment.* Like a fear-starter-kit of sorts. The rest of 'em? We make them here! Then our sales team goes out and markets them to the general public."

"A sales force? You have a sales force?" I said skeptically.

"Of course we do! Fears just don't happen, they have to be manufactured and then sold to people because..." Sturgess stopped mid-sentence, tapped his chin several times with an index finger. "It's really isn't my place to go into all of this. I know! You should take the tour!"
"The tour?! How big is this place?" I stammered.

"Do you have any idea how many fears there are?" he asked.

I shook my head, no.

"To date, we've scientifically confirmed the creation of over 522 fears, with another 117 on the drawing board and 42 more that are patent pending! And each fear has its own department - well, almost. Last year they merged alureaphobia with signaphobia – oy, vey, what a disaster! Almost got one of the Fear Masters fired!"

"Alura-what?"

"Sorry," said Sturgess. "Aluraphobia, the fear of cats and dogs, and signaphobia, the fear of... well... *signs!* They won't be doing that again anytime soon!" he snorted.

My head was absolutely spinning; none of this made any sense! But I had to admit, I was intrigued. And, as Sturgess had pointed out, time was not an issue.

"So, how do I take this tour?" I asked.

"Simple. Just go back out the way you came," Sturgess said, pointing a crooked finger at the door I had entered through minutes earlier. "If I'm not mistaken, there's a tour that's just about to start."

Chapter Six: Allison

"Good morning, everyone. Welcome to The Fear Factory!" The voice came from a stunningly beautiful brunette who looked more like a fashion model than a tour guide. "My name is Allison and I'm delighted to be your guide."
A group of approximately 20 people – some old, some young, some dressed in suits, others in pajamas and looking like they'd just rolled out of bed – stood in a semi-circle, listening intently and hanging on the woman's every word.

"Are there any questions before we start?"
Any questions? Is she serious? I had so many questions I didn't know where to begin! But I opted to stay tight-lipped and just listen.

"This facility develops and distributes one of the most powerful emotions known to man, that emotion being fear. Fear is an unpleasant feeling of perceived danger, real or not, and is considered one of the five basic emotions." As she said this a large glass screen was lowered from the ceiling and came to life, glowing bright yellow in the darkened room.
"The five basic emotions are anger... sadness... hate... happiness... and our favorite, of course... fear! And our mission here is simple..." The scene turned from soft yellow to crimson red and the words Fear Factory Mission Statement appeared.

"...*to manufacture and market limiting thoughts and beliefs to the masses in order to debilitate, destroy, and deny emotional health and happiness... one fear at a time!* This is what we do! And, if you'll allow me to brag just a bit, we do it very, very well."

This is insane, I thought as Allison addressed the group as if we were all third graders. "So," she continued, "who can tell me what a phobia is?"

"It's another word for fear?" offered an elderly woman in a lavender sweater.

"That's right," Allison said with a smile. "Phobia is simply another word for fear, but it's a little more complicated than that. A fear is either the realization of a threat, or the mere expectation of danger. Like, for example, you're walking down the street and suddenly a large dog jumps out at you!"

As she said this Allison suddenly lunged toward a small boy wearing a baseball cap, causing him to jump and let out a yelp, the entire group breaking into laughter.

"You see how he jumped? That's because fear is a necessary ingredient for survival in all animals, an involuntary reflex built into the human system. It allows us to respond to danger through a chemical rush of adrenaline that jolts the body into action.

So that when you pass a darkened alley late at night, the fear you feel that someone might jump out at you helps make you faster, more focused, stronger… or at least more ready to run!" Allison pulled two tootsie pops from her pocket and held them out to the boy. "Cherry or grape?" The boy reached out and snatched both suckers from her hand, once again to the group's laughter.

"What you just witnessed is commonly known as the fight-or-flight syndrome. And it is this system – one originally designed to help you – that we exploit. The fear that was designed ages ago to prepare a person for physical survival in the wild is no longer necessary for survival in the office or shopping mall.

"You don't know my boss." a woman joked to the group's laughter. But Allison just pressed on.

"In today's society, a phobia can best be described as a persistent, illogical fear. To explain it better, why don't we go to the Fundamentals of Phobias exhibit? It's right this way! And we're walking… and we're walking…"

Allison led the group down the hall and stopped in front of a wall that contained descriptions, diagrams, and various other exhibits. It looked very much like something you'd find at a natural history museum. The tour was weird yet somehow fascinating, and soon I forgot all about Fearn International, Doug, and the presentation.

"The term *'phobia'* is used to describe an irrational, often disabling fear that psychologists divide into three specific sub-categories, the first being agoraphobia." Allison pointed to a chart on the wall. The chart read: Three Categories of Phobias: Agoraphobia. Social Phobias. Specific Phobias. And underneath it read: *Copyright, The Fear Factory.*

"Agoraphobia is a fear of leaving your home or familiar safe surroundings, and the panic attack that usually follows. It is the only phobia that has a category all to itself because it is the only phobia that is regularly treated as a medical condition. Of course, agoraphobia should not be confused with <u>ang</u>oraphobia, which is the fear of overly soft sweaters!"
I laughed loud and hard, causing Allison to look my way.

"Just a little Fear Factory humor!" she said with a playful smile. "Now, if you'll follow me a few steps to your right…" Allison turned and led the group a little further down the hallway.

"The second category of phobias are the Social Phobias; fears that have to do with other people and social relationships."

"Like what?" asked a large, muscular African-American man in an Oakland Raiders football jersey.

"An example? Sir, we have an entire hall full of them."

Chapter Seven: The Hall of Fears

Allison turned and led the group down the hallway and through a set of heavy glass doors with a sign overhead which read, *The Hall of Fears.* Once the entire group was gathered in the center of the room, Allison snapped her fingers and the lights in the room began to dim. Next, a set of projectors dropped from the ceiling and the names of assorted fears began appearing on the walls around us, revolving around us like planets circling the sun. It was a stunning sight which put any PowerPoint presentation I'd ever seen to shame. One couldn't help but be impressed by The Fear Factory's attention to detail.

"Social Phobias run the gamut, including thinking people are watching or staring at you, speaking in front of clients and co-workers, introducing yourself to others, meeting strangers, going to new places and having new experiences, even eating in public." Allison said. "One of my personal favorites is called telephoneophobia, or the fear of using the telephone."

Allison described the thrill of watching a fear factory training tape of a woman who was so afraid of the telephone that even the thought of calling to order a pizza made her heart almost jump out of her chest.

"She thought that she'd be putting the other person out by taking her order, even though it was their job to do exactly that. It got so bad that eventually the fear ruined her career and literally destroyed her life. Like I said, this is one of my personal favorites."

And though Allison seemed almost gleeful telling the group about this woman's debilitating fear, there was empathy in her eyes for the immense tragic pain she was describing.

"And, finally, we have the category we call Specific Phobias, which are just what they sound like; specific panic triggers that bring on fear. This includes things like the fear of heights, spiders, flying, even cats and dogs."

"Alureaphobia," I blurted.

"Very good, Mr....?"

"Traynor, Steven Traynor," I said, my mouth suddenly going dry as Allison smiled the most radiant smile in my direction.

"Mr. Traynor is quite correct! Alureaphobia, the fear of cats and dogs." Then, with another snap of her fingers virtually every inch of all four walls were filled with a sea of fears and their phobic definitions. Sturgess was right – there were hundreds and hundreds of fears. It was both amazing and disturbing, all at once.

The man in the Oakland Raiders jersey raised his hand and said,

"I've got a question. Personally, I have no fears. But I can't help but wonder if it's possible for other people to ever overcome their fears?"

"Oh my, we certainly hope not," Allison quipped. "If they do overcome them, as you put it, then we didn't do our job very well and it's back to the drawing board." The big guy did not look pleased with her answer.

"This seems like a good time to let you browse the list of specific phobias. So here is your assignment: take fifteen minutes to review the list and see which phobias afflict you personally. Then we'll get back together and discuss them."
The list on the wall ran in alphabetical order, and, being the organized person I am, I decided to start with the A's and work my way through the entire list. As I went I did as instructed, making a list of the phobias that I personally suffered from.

When I was done I was shocked and dismayed to discover there were seventeen different fears listed on my note pad! And, while not all of them were debilitating, I had to admit that each negatively affected my life, at least to some degree.

While the walls in the hall of fears were covered with names of all the typical fears you'd expect to see on such a list (things like open spaces, heights, failure, rejection, flying, mice, snakes, and computers) there were many that I'd never even heard of:

Amnesiaphobia – the fear of amnesia.

Dendrophobia – the fear of trees.

Meteorphobia – the fear of meteors.

Russophobia – the fear of Russians.

There was even Phobiaphobia... *the fear of phobias!*

It was fascinating to see some of the strange things that people were afraid of. Then I felt the warmth of a hand on my shoulder and Allison's voice from behind me.

"So, Mr. Traynor, what exactly are you afraid of?"

Chapter Eight: Learning My F.F.I.

I turned around and saw Allison standing there, feeling heat rise in my body.

"Call me Steven," I managed, dabbing perspiration from my forehead.

"Very well, Steven. The question still stands."

"Well, I don't like spiders and snakes," I sang in a joking fashion to the tune of the old Jerry Stafford song from the 70's.

"Spiders, snakes, heights, enclosed spaces; these are things that most people are afraid of," she said, apparently unimpressed with my singing ability. "What I'm asking is: *What are the fears that are uniquely yours?*"

"Nothing much, really," I lied. "At least nothing that negatively impacts my life."

"That's interesting, because your F.F.I. indicates otherwise," she stated.

"My F-F-I?" I asked.

"Yes, your Fear Factor Index, or F.F.I . It's a combination of all your fears, cross-referenced against the level of debilitation for each."

She knew every one of my fears!

There was something very unnerving about the knowledge that someone - especially this beautiful woman, Allison - would know my deepest fears, let alone sit around and analyze them.

"I have a fear chart?" was all I could manage.

"They run a fear chart on everyone. How else would the Fear Masters identify opportunities for additional fear implantation? And if you don't mind me saying," she continued, "compared to most people, your FFI isn't totally off-the-chart - but I would hardly classify it as nothing serious. Anything that keeps you from being your best and living your dreams is serious."

This was going from bad to worse.

"Would you like to see your chart?" she asked. "I can pull it up on the screen."

"No, that's okay," I said. "I know each of my fears intimately. I don't need to see them graphically displayed." We stood there in silence for several long seconds. Then I began thinking about her question, and the fact that she'd already seen my chart.

"If you already knew what my fears were," I asked Allison, "then why did you ask me earlier what they were?"

Allison smiled sheepishly, looked away for a moment, then back at me. "Well, I guess I wanted to see if you were willing to open up to me." This was good and bad; good, because Allison seemed to be interested in me, but bad, because I had apparently failed her test. I vowed to myself to be more open with Allison from now on, no matter what she asked, no matter how embarrassing.

"Okay," I said with all the confidence I could muster. "Let's take a look at my chart."

"Really? You want to?"

"Sure," I said, "why not? How bad could it be?"

"Display fear chart for T. Traynor, d.o.b. 12/2/65, on monitor HOF7 please," Allison said to no one in particular. Then, within seconds, a graph appeared on the wall monitor and the answer to the question, 'How bad could it be?' was answered, right before my eyes. An enormous bar-graph which illustrated twelve prominent fears, each in a different color for maximum impact, was displayed.

"Well, at least it's only twelve," I joked.

"They only look at the top twelve, referred to in The Fear Factory as the 'Debilitating Dozen'.

"Cute," I replied. But it didn't seem cute at all – it was downright discouraging.

"Don't feel bad," Allison said with encouragement. "The vast majority of people refuse to even look at their chart."

"I did refuse," I reminded her.

"True, but then you did it anyway!"

Her attempts at making me feel better weren't working, because my fear chart said it all.

Right there in front of me were all the things I knew were stumbling blocks to the life I wanted to live, things I worked hard at avoiding, like flying... and public speaking... and failure and rejection... and trying anything new. And, for the first time in a long time, I was forced to face the truth; there was battle going on in my head which would determine my future.

Chapter Nine: A Career in Fear

"So, Allison, what are *you* afraid of?" She looked away, seemingly uncomfortable with the question. "I showed you mine," I said with a smile. "Come on, how bad could it be?" She turned back, looked me in the eye.

"You're right - I *do* know your fears. And, in fairness, you deserve to know mine." She glanced down at the floor for a moment, bit her lip. "It was me."

"What do you mean? What are you talking about, what was you?"

"The woman I told the group about today," Allison said, still looking down, "the one in the training video who I said was so terrified of the telephone. That woman was me." Neither of us knew what to say next, so we simply said nothing. Finally, Allison looked up and broke the silence.

"For as long as I can remember people have told me how beautiful I am. But, for whatever reason, I have never been able to see it. Even when I started modeling I would look at the other girls and feel so inferior I dreaded even being around them."

That's when it hit me. I *had* seen Allison before, many times in fact, on the cover of fashion magazines. Some of the ads were probably ours, produced by Ramsden+Media. Then, one day, she simply disappeared.

"But you really are beautiful." I said. "Stunning!"

"Please, Steven, you don't have to…"

"No, really," I said, interrupting her. "Since the first moment I saw you I've been… mesmerized."

"Well, when I look in the mirror, I don't see anything close to mesmerizing. I see… *plain.* Anyway, in addition to feeling ugly, I decided to buy a phone fear, a serious one. It reached a point that every time the phone would ring, I'd be afraid to answer it, even though I knew it might be my agent with another assignment. Eventually, I stopped answering the phone altogether. Next thing I knew I was afraid to make outbound calls, too. Then I stopped opening my mail. Before I knew it, I had literally closed myself off to the world."

This was tragic, I thought.

"How did you end up here?" I finally asked.

"Me? I stumbled in here just like you did, came in through the dark room, met Sturgess and took the tour. Only difference between us is that you'll probably leave. I didn't. I don't know how to explain it, but The Fear Factory just felt like home. So I never left. Eventually, they offered me the tour guide position, and here we are. You could say I stopped modeling and chose a career in fear."

My God! Staying in The Fear Factory forever and never leaving was something I hadn't contemplated, but I could see how it could happen. You just got used to it.

Allison forced a smile, putting on a brave face.

"Fears are almost endless, you know. In fact, at The Fear Factory, we've turned the process of creating fear terms into something of a game. All you have to do is take the Greek word for something and add the suffix 'phobia' at the end, and you get a new phobic term. For example, you take the Greek word for insects – entomo - and then you add phobia, and, voila! Entoemophobia! The fear of bugs! See, it's easy! You try one." It was clear that Allison was changing the subject, lightening the mood, so I decided not to push it and simply played along.

"Okay," I said, "What's the Greek word for books?"

"Biblio," she said.

"So the fear of books is Bibliophobia?"

"Yes! Now, if you want to have some fun, just put any word up front - it doesn't have to be Greek at all. Tell me something you don't like about shopping."

"I don't know, how about being badgered by peppy salespeople?"

"Easy," she declared: "Gap-o-phobia."

"That's funny," I said, laughing.

"Give me something else you don't like," she said.

"Okay, pepperoni."

"That's easy - Pizzaphobia!"

"You should go on *What's Your Phobia?*" I said jokingly.

"Oh, I would," Allison said, seriously, "but employees aren't allowed."

"I was kidding. There really is a show called *What's Your Phobia?*"

"Sure. It comes on right after *Who Wants To Be a Scaredy Cat?* Now it's your turn. How about the fear of winning a contest and not being at home to accept the prize?"

"EdMcMahonophobia!" I declared.

"See, you could work here!" We both laughed so hard our sides hurt.

After getting control of myself I said, "Earlier, when I asked about overcoming fears, you made a joke. Seriously, Allison, I really want to know how to do it. It's important to me." Allison looked at me with serious eyes, leaned in and whispered: "I wasn't joking. We don't talk about cures here - not ever! It's... *dangerous.*"

"Dangerous? How?"

"It just is."

"But you don't understand, Allison. I..."

"I don't understand? You think I don't understand? Trust me, Steven, I understand. Sometimes I'm not sure where my fears stop and I begin!" she said, almost shouting the words.

"That's what I'm afraid of, Allison! Sometimes my fears feel like they're alive in me, like they're... *growing.* Like my fear of making presentations to groups; if I don't get control of it, I'm going to lose my job. Please, Allison, is there anything you can tell me?"

Allison bit her lip, appeared to be deep in thought, struggling with herself. Then: "Well, they might have something available over at *Courage Crafters, Inc.,* but..."

"*Courage Crafters?* What's that?"

"I'm sorry, Steven, I can't say anymore. I've said too much already."

"Is it a place? Where is it? What do they do?"

"If you want to know more, go to Sturgess. Maybe he'll tell you," she said, straightening her jacket and standing erect. "Now, if you'll excuse me, I've got a tour to lead." And with that she simply walked away.

Chapter Ten: The Fear Masters

By the time I caught up to Allison she was already back in full tour-mode. "Let's see a show of hands of those of you who could identify at least ten fears you personally suffer from," she said. Almost every hand went up, including my own.

"How about twenty or more?" she continued.

Several hands went up.

"Thirty or more?" Allison pressed. No one raised their hand.

"Okay, let me see a show of hands of those of you who have a fear of raising your hand?" Allison quipped. The group broke into nervous laughter. "Personally, I have 9 major fears and 37 minor fears for a total Fear Factor Index of 142.9. So, if you've got multiple fears, don't be embarrassed. Once again, anyone with 30 or more? Let's see those hands!"
Several hands slowly went into the air.

"That's better! Remember, you bought your fears, so wear them with pride."

Watching Allison work the group, it was hard to understand how such a beautiful creature with so much poise and confidence could be plagued with so many fears.

"Next, I've got a special treat for you! We've arranged for you to spend some time in The Fear Factory main auditorium with one of our resident Fear Masters, Professor Ralph Kornbluth. Professor Kornbluth is one of only six fear development professionals to have earned the Fear Master designation, sort of like a Ph.D. in Fearology. So, if you'll all just follow me."

Like everything else at The Fear Factory, the auditorium was state-of-the-art in every way, including two large screens on each side of the stage that projected the image of Professor Kornbluth as he addressed the group.

"Good day, everyone. My name is Professor Ralph Kornbluth," said the tall, gray-haired man with sharp features and piercing eyes, "and I've been asked to share some information on the application of fear. I promise to try my best not to sound like a stuffy intellectual." No one laughed, probably because it was clear that Kornbluth *was* a stuffy intellectual.

"The term phobia from the Greek word for fear, *fobos*," he continued, "is used to denote any number of psycho-logical and physio-logical conditions. Some suffer from little more than mild anxiety and quirks. Others suffer full-fledged panic attacks with all the associated disabling symptoms, including intense fear, paranoia and sheer terror."

Was it my imagination, or did the corners of Kornbluth's lips just turn up in a slight smile when he said this?

"People with phobias usually treat them by avoiding the thing they fear, which is fine by us," Kornbluth continued. "Let me be perfectly clear about one thing; the mission of The Fear Factory is not to scare... *the goal is to debilitate!* To implant enough fears to alter people's pattern of living and their chances for a happy, successful life. If you avoid the things you fear, and, in the process, you do less of the things you love and achieve fewer of your goals and dreams, then we've done our jobs!" Kornbluth was a ball of laughs. And he wasn't finished:

"According to a recent survey paid for by The Fear Factory Ad Council, but conducted by an independent outside research organization, we currently enjoy a market penetration of 81.5% of Americans who suffer from some form of phobia. And we're especially effective with women and men over the age of 25."

Kornbluth was on a roll, spitting out information without taking a breath. "Some fears are universal and timeless; failure, rejection, spiders, heights, flying, public speaking, death, going to the dentist, etc., these will always be the core of our business, while others come and go, rise and fall in popularity, with the times.

"For example, two hundred years ago we had great success with the fear of being buried alive. Today? People hardly give it a thought! On the other hand, eating bugs was a normal activity for people for thousands of years, so there was no fear of it. But, thanks to the popularity of the TV show Fear Factory, which I'm proud to say is produced in studio 13 right down the hall; we're making great strides with the fear of insects."

"Why don't you share the top ten fears with the group, professor," Allison prompted.

"Ah! Allison knows I'm a big Dave Letterman fan! Okay, here goes; in order of percentage of population affected, here are The Fear Factory's *Top Ten* fears…

#10… Neckrophobia… the fear of death.

#9… Dentophobia… the fear of dentists.

#8… Neophobia… the fear of anything new.

#7… Altophobia… the fear of heights.

#6… Odinophobia… the fear of pain.

#5… Claustrophobia… the fear of enclosed spaces.

#4… Glossophobia… the fear of speaking in public, a previous #1 chart-topper!

#3… Atichiphobia… the fear of failure, a personal favorite.

#2… Aviophobia… the fear of flying, really the fear of crashing, but that's splitting hairs!

And the #1 Fear on the planet… *Arachnaphopia!* The fear of spiders!

"For further reinforcement with arachnophobia we issued a press release last year saying that the average person swallows nine spiders a year while they're sleeping! Boy, did we get a good bump in the numbers with that one!" Kornbluth said, clapping his hands together with excitement.

"Is that true?" I turned to see the elderly woman in the lavender sweater, her eyes wide with horror.

"Who knows, and who cares!" Kornbluth shot back. "The only thing that matters is that you believe it. Seriously, the look on your face was priceless!"

Then a question came from a teenage girl. "What's your favorite fear, professor?"

"My favorite? That's easy. I hope you'll allow me this one dalliance into self-aggrandizement as this happens to be a fear that I personally created – *it's the fear of success!*"

Allison jumped in like a color-commentator on Monday Night Football. "The fear of success just won the fear of the year award! Over the years it's really taken hold. In fact, The Fear Factory just held a huge 100 year anniversary celebration for the fear of success in June."

A man in the front row raised his hand and asked, "What has been the biggest discovery at The Fear Factory?"

"According to psychologists," Kornbluth answered, "approximately 10% of people's fears are based on real, tangible dangers like someone pointing a loaded gun in your direction. Which means the other 90% are imagined. Then Carol Spinkowski, who used to work in insectophobia, transferred over to allodoxaphobia, which by the way is the fear of opinions, located in the *Imagined Fears* division over in the East Tower.

"Spinkowski found a way to take imagined fears that are not truly a threat to health or safety, and to make them feel like they were real. Let me tell you, that was a seminal moment. Then Frank Lawson over in Fear Leverage, created a process called Visualization of Future Consequences... or V.F.C. for short. VFC took Carol's creation to the next level and increased LOD by 143%."

"LOD?" asked the burly guy in the Oakland Raiders jersey. "Sorry, bad habit," said Kornbluth.

"Seems the bigger a corporation grows, the more we tend to speak in acronyms. L.O.D. stands for level of debilitation. When a fear first takes hold it adds to our fear conversion number, which is a yes/no thing. Yes, the fear took hold, or, no, it didn't. But LOD measures the level of debilitation within the person, kind of a multiplier if you will.

Frank's visualization process took the LOD numbers off the chart."

"How does fear visualization work?" I asked.

"That's the beauty of it. What Frank did was take an existing program that's already part of the human brain, designed to help people to visualize success and happiness, and created a virus that makes people imagine failure and danger instead. Amazing, huh?" This guy was really starting to get on my nerves.

"Of course, when we can, we try to debilitate with an SDF - oops, I did it again, to quote Britney Spears. I mean a *Single Debilitating Fear*, like agoraphobia for example. Let's face it, you can get around the fear of alligators pretty easily – just don't go to Florida! But you use an effective single debilitating fear, like the fear of going out your front door, and you've pretty much ruined someone's life!"

"Unfortunately, only a small portion of the general public is susceptible to SDFs, so we implant a high volume of lesser impact fears in the hope that, collectively, they do the trick. Right, professor?" Allison prompted.

"Yes, that's exactly right, Allison. We simply try to overwhelm people with lots of little fears. You could say we're like that one hour eyeglass place, *Lens Crafters*, but instead of helping the world to see, we're helping the world to flee."

This suddenly made me remember something Allison had said earlier. "Professor, what can you tell us about *Courage Crafters?*" I called out.

At first Kornbluth simply looked agitated and then flustered. He looked at Allison, who quickly lowered her eyes. Then Kornbluth glanced at his watch and said, "I'm sorry, it seems we've run out of time. Enjoy the rest of your tour!"

And without another word, Kornbluth rushed off the stage like it had suddenly caught on fire. I leaned over to Allison and whispered in her ear.

"Run out of time?" I said quietly. "I thought there was no time in *The Fear Factory*."

"There isn't," Allison replied. "There isn't."

Chapter Eleven: Sullivan & Ainsworth

The end of the afternoon was spent with two Fear Factory department heads; Susan Sullivan of Sales & Marketing, and Peter Ainsworth in Self-Limiting Beliefs. Sullivan went first.

"I'm sure Allison has explained that the human brain only comes with three standard fears, but the rest of the fears need to be sold. If we don't sell the fears that are created, this place goes out of business. Not that we're jealous or anything, but let's be honest; we do all the work, and the fear masters get all the glory." As she said this Sullivan's face turned a slight crimson and she massaged the veins along her neck which had clearly begun to pulse.

"But how do you sell a fear?" asked a tall man with fire-engine red hair.

"Excellent question. Tell me, what business are you in?" Sullivan asked.

"My company manufactures automotive after-market products which we wholesale through outside distributors," the man answered.

"That's where I was on my way to today, to make a sales presentation to a group of distributors – until I got hijacked and ended up here." Sounds familiar, I thought.

"Well, that's where The Fear Factory is different," Sullivan responded. "Though we manufacture fears, we don't use wholesalers or brokers. Instead we sell direct to the public, and we try to make our pitch at the moment of greatest susceptibility – the triggering event."

"The triggering event? What's that?" the big man in the Raiders jersey asked. For some reason the hulk of a guy looked familiar to me, but I couldn't figure out why.

"Virtually all fears – other than the three that come as standard equipment – can usually be traced back to a specific, traumatic experience, often at an early age, but not necessarily," Sullivan said. "This is the moment of greatest susceptibility, what we call the triggering event."

"But how do you create the triggering event?" the man asked.

"That's the beauty of it!" Sullivan declared. "We don't! There's no way to anticipate or control the events themselves. We simply wait for the events to happen and, when they do, a Fear Factory sales rep gets there as soon as possible, sometimes within milliseconds."

"And the sales rep implants the fear in the person?" I asked Sullivan.

"Well, not exactly. 'Implant' suggests that we surgically install the fear in the person's brain, and it doesn't work quite like that. Our reps simply provide possible interpretations of what the event could mean to the person. For example," Sullivan said, turning to a young man in his twenties: "What do you do for a living, young man?"

"I sell suits," he said.

"Okay. Let's imagine a customer told you to your face that he wanted a more experienced salesperson help him. If that happened, what would you think?"

"I don't know. I'd probably be confused as to why he felt that way."

"Exactly. And in that moment of confusion, as you were trying to interpret the meaning of the event, one of our reps would show up with a four-color Fear Factory brochure and 'sell' you one or more interpretations of the event, each designed to create self-doubt, lowered self-esteem, and ultimately fear!

"In a situation like this," Sullivan continued, "the rep might sell you on the idea that you were too young… or too inexperienced… or not dressed properly… or perhaps all of the above. Of course, immediately after the recipient has chosen their interpretation, they often begin feeling discouraged and depressed.

That's where Peter's department comes in. Peter?"

Sullivan took a seat and a short, pudgy man in his mid-fifties stepped before the group.

"Hello, my name is Peter Ainsworth. As Susan said, my department provides a virtually endless stream of after-market products designed to enhance the self-limiting belief that's just been purchased, specifically negative self-talk, excuses and blame. In short, we help people articulate how they're feeling. That's about it. Any questions?"

Unlike Sullivan, Ainsworth wasn't the chatty, charming sort. So Allison jumped in to prod Ainsworth along.

"Peter, tell the group some of the phrases your department has written."

"Well, I don't know…"

"Come on, Peter, just a few?"

"Okay, let's see. My department wrote… *if it's not one thing it's another… you just can't win… no good deed goes unpunished… just my luck… I should have known… nothing good ever happens to me… here we go again… nobody loves me…* and… *I'm such an idiot!* Oh, yeah - and the *Dummies* book series – that was our idea, too."

"Peter's department also does excuses." Allison added.

"Stop it, Allison, you're embarrassing me. But we are pleased with some of them. Let's see, we're really proud of... *I got caught in traffic... s/he did it, not me... the economy is experiencing a downturn... I didn't have enough time... my dog ate my homework,* and *I shot the sheriff, but I did not shoot the deputy,* though those last two were originally written as jokes. Who knew someone would actually use them. So, does anyone have any questions?"

"I have one for Ms. Sullivan," I said. "What percentage of sales opportunities do you actually close?"

"Our closure rate is a very impressive 83.2%... Due in large part to the training each Fear Factory rep receives at FFU."

"FFU?" Asked the guy in the Raider's jersey.

"Fear Factory University. It's a three week, advanced course in fear sales and implementation."

"But that leaves 16.8% that don't get closed," I continued, pressing the issue. "How do *those* people manage to reject the fear?" This is what I really wanted to know. But the question must have struck a nerve, for Sullivan and Ainsworth froze in place... glanced nervously at one another... speechless.

Finally, Sullivan spoke: "It's very complicated and far too technical for the time we've got available."

Ainsworth, taking the cue, quickly glanced at his watch. "Susan, don't we have a meeting with the people in failure and rejection?"

"Why, yes, we do!"

And with that, both Sullivan and Ainsworth jumped to their feet and fled the stage. As the pair hurried from the room, I couldn't help but think: *two more fear factory employees with no time to answer tough questions in a place where, supposedly, time did not exist.*

Chapter Twelve: Just Win, Baby!

Just because there was no time *per se*, that didn't mean I didn't feel it passing. So I was particularly glad when Allison told the group that break time had arrived.

"We've arranged to have sleeping rooms for each of you, and while you'll be sharing with another member of the group, I think you'll find the accommodations quite comfortable. This will give you a chance to relax, freshen up, even take a nap if you want. Then you're all invited to the scared to death lounge for happy hour. And, to make it fun, everyone is required to dress up as their most debilitating fear! Just stop by The Fear Factory costume department and tell them your fear – they have a costume for just about everything!" The strange had just become truly bizarre.

Allison was right about the accommodations; even the dorm at The Fear Factory was state-of-the-art, each room complete with a wide-screen plasma TV, whirl-pool style tub, and a complimentary, fully-stocked mini bar.

Clearly there was a lot of money to be made by peddling anxiety, fear and panic. I grabbed a diet coke and the TV remote, and then plopped in one of the two queen-sized beds. Any chance of getting CNN or FOX News? I wondered. It was not to be.

Showing on channel 2 was *Fear Factory Today*. Channel 3 had a game show called *What's Your Phobia?* On channel 4 I found *Oprah!* Today's topic? Accepting your limitations, loving your fears. Channel 5, *The Fear Is Right!* Channel 6 had live coverage of the annual *Fear Factor Marathon*. On and on it went... 134 channels of nothing but fear.

"Enough fear for one day," I said aloud and turned off the TV. Seconds later the large man in the Oakland Raiders jersey appeared in the doorway.

"Looks like we're roommates," he said, closing the door behind him and reaching out his giant hand. "My name is Winston Clark, but you can call me Win." That's when it hit me.

"Oh, my God, you're Big Win Clark! You're the linebacker for the Oakland Raiders!" I exclaimed, extending my hand which disappeared in his massive paw. "I'm Steven Traynor, one of your biggest fans!"

"You may not be a fan after tonight," the big man said with a laugh. "My teammates say I snore like a freight train."

"No problem," I said. "I'm a pretty deep sleeper." I couldn't believe it. I was standing in a room with Winston Elliott Clark, a pro football icon who earned the nickname 'Big Win' after rushing for three touchdowns in the Raiders Super Bowl win.

And here he was, my roommate at The Fear Factory! Go figure.

"You look like a smart guy, Steve, so tell me; you figure this thing out yet?" Win asked.

"What do you mean?"

"This," he said with a wave of the hand, "this… place! The whole thing. I mean, one minute I get called into the Coach's office, and next thing I know I'm standing in a dark hallway. Just weird, man."

"Well, I know why I'm here," I said.

"You do?" said Win.

"Yeah. I'm pretty sure I'm here to confront my fears, and somehow this place holds the key. The real question is: What is a fearless guy like *you* doing here?"

Win stayed quiet, hung his giant head and sat on the opposite bed. "Can you keep a secret?" the big man asked.

"Yeah, sure," I said.

"Truth is, I'm riddled with fear," he admitted.

"Really? Like what?" I asked in disbelief.

"Tons of things. I'm afraid of gettin' old… afraid of gettin' fat…"

"We're all afraid of that!" I interjected. But Win wasn't done:

"…I'm afraid of losin'… afraid of gettin' cut… and what if my knees go, man? How do I make a living and provide for my family then? And the biggest fear of all - what if people forget who I am after my playin' days are over? Sometimes I think I'm nothing *but* fear," he said dejectedly.

"You're not alone," I said. "Hey, you want to go grab a drink?"

"Yeah, sounds good. Give me few minutes to rest my eyes and we'll head out," Win replied, laying his big head on what looked like a miniature pillow. And within thirty seconds Big Win Clark, one of my biggest heroes in the world, was out like a light and indeed snoring like a freight train.

Laying there, listening to Win snore, I couldn't get this *Courage Crafters* place out of my head. What was it? What did they do? More importantly, why were so many Fear Factory employees reluctant to even talk about it? Then I remembered Allison's response when I'd pressed her for details. 'Ask Sturgess' she had said.

So, before I had a chance to talk myself out of it, I jumped off the bed and headed out, closing the door quietly behind me. And as I started down the hall, I realized I didn't really know how to find Sturgess' office. But, determined to talk with the man, I set out for my own little tour of The Fear Factory.

Chapter Thirteen: Searching for Answers

When Sturgess said The Fear Factory was big, he wasn't kidding. I started retracing the path from the dormitory building back to sales and marketing, then to the main auditorium, and from there back to the hall of fears.

When I got to where I thought the gray door should be, I found nothing but a solid wall. I was sure I was in the right place, but obviously I was wrong. I decided to keep following the hallway as far as it would go.

As I kept walking I noticed something strange happening... the further down the hall I went, the darker it got... as if someone was turning a dimmer switch with each step I took. Eventually, I reached a point where it became so dark, it became difficult to see. Then I took one more step and I was in total darkness. And, although it was pitch black, I knew exactly where I was...

I was in the dark room.

I placed my hands on the wall and felt around until, just as I had earlier in the day, I found the door. I turned the knob, pulled the door open, and once again light streamed into the hall. At this moment I fully expected to hear Sturgess yell for me to close the door, but all was silent.

"Mr. Sturgess?" I called out, looking around, seeing his chair was empty. Once again, the bright red door across the room caught my eye. Maybe he's back there, I thought, walking to the door and turning the knob.

Locked.

But, just as I turned to leave, I noticed that Sturgess had left his computer running. And he was logged on!

Now, while I pride myself as being a person with high integrity, I hadn't come this far to not get answers. So, just as I had earlier that morning, I took a seat at Miles Sturgess' computer and started pecking at the keyboard, with no idea of what I was looking for or what I would find. All I knew was that there was more to this Fear Factory place than they were willing to share… and this was as good a place as any to start looking.

Chapter Fourteen: The Decision

Walking into the *Scared to Death Lounge* was like walking into the biggest Halloween party you could imagine. Hundreds of people, each in costume, laughing and drinking and dancing up a storm. In addition to knowing how to make people scared, The Fear Factory definitely knew how to party.

That's when I realized that, with everyone in costume it was going to be difficult to find Allison. I scanned the room with my eyes, watched as someone dressed like a large spider danced with a computer monitor, and someone dressed as a prison convict sat at the bar, having drinks with someone dressed as an airplane.

The problem was solved seconds later when a large telephone receiver with two shapely legs sticking out of the bottom approached. It was Allison.

"You're not in costume!" she protested.

"Yes, I am," I declared. "You said to come as the thing that scared us most. Well, the thing that scares me most is me!" It occurred to me, as the words left my lips, that I wasn't kidding; I was scared of who I'd become, and also who I'd never become if I didn't get my fears under control.

"That's cheating! Anyway, are you hungry? We've got great crab puffs, unless you're afraid of shellfish, too!" Allison took my hand and led me to a large table covered with appetizers.

"I found Courage Crafters," I said flatly. The telephone receiver stopped dead in its tracks, let go of my hand.

"What do you mean? How?"

"You said to ask Sturgess, so I did. Well, not exactly. He wasn't there, so I went on his computer and..."

"You did what?!?" she interjected.

"I went on his computer, and it was all there!" I said. "You're never going to believe where it's located, Allison!" After a moment the shock wore off and Allison's curiosity finally got the better of her.

"Where?" she asked.

"It's... right... next... door! And not only had that, I found out that The Fear Factory and Courage Crafters are connected by a sky bridge! There were blueprints for both buildings in the computer – I printed them out! I really think I can get us there."

"Us? Oh, no! You're not dragging me into this!"

"Come on Allison, I need your help."

"What you are doing is very dangerous. What if you get caught?"

"Get caught? So what if I get caught! What are the Fear Masters going to do, throw me in The Fear Factory dungeon?" As I said this I suddenly felt a twinge of fear course through me. Maybe there *was* a fear factory dungeon! Knowing this place, it was entirely plausible! Then I thought, no, that's just your fear talking. This is something you have to do! "I don't care what happens, Allison. I've made up my mind and I'm going! Now, are you in, or are you out?"

"I'm in!" a deep voice from behind me said. I turned around to find a large letter "L" (apparently for 'loser') standing behind me, two big feet sticking out of the bottom. It was Win, his face protruding from a hole in the top.

"Yes!" I shouted, holding up my hand to high-five him, but with no hands all Win could do was smile and nod at me. "Come on, Allison, join the team!" I challenged.

"Yeah, join the team," Win encouraged.
But Allison just stood there, glaring. And I got the message loud and clear as I the telephone receiver turned and walked away.

"So, what exactly have I gotten myself into?" Win asked.

"First, we're going to find a sky bridge," I said with a determination I'd forgotten I possessed. "And then we're going to find our courage."

Chapter Fifteen: The Sky Bridge

Finding the sky bridge was a lot harder than finding Sturgess' office and took us considerably longer than I thought it would. It was like making your way through a maze. But, then again, with no time to worry about, it was just a matter of doing it.

"You sure you know where we're going?" Win asked for the third time.

"No, Win, I'm not sure of anything in this crazy place, but according to the blueprint there should be a stairway right about here." I turned around in a circle, looking in every direction. Nothing.

"Maybe they hid it," Win suggested.

"Hid it? Hid it how?"

Win shrugged his massive shoulders. "Beats me. You're the smart guy, I'm just the muscle."

I studied the printed copy of the blueprint once again and walked to the spot where the stairway should have been and knocked on the wall, took a step to my left, and knocked again. And again. The fourth knock sounded different.

"Win, you're a genius!" I declared. "They walled the stairway off so we couldn't find it! Now, all we've got to do is find a way to break through to the other side!"

"You sure that's where it is?" Win asked, pointing to the spot in the wall.

"I'm positive!" I replied. "Why?"

"Just stand back," was all Win said. Then, as if taking a handoff from an imaginary quarterback, Big Win Clark charged toward the wall. A jolt of fear surged through me; *what if I'm wrong?* What if there's nothing but brick back there! Win lowered his shoulder and smashed into the wall... and right through it... disappearing through a cartoon-like hole in the plaster. A moment later Win reappeared, dusting pieces of plaster from his massive shoulders.

"You comin'?" he asked with that million-dollar-smile of his.

We climbed three flights of stairs and, just like the blueprints suggested, there it was: a glass-enclosed sky bridge that stretched into an endless sea of darkness.

"Let's do this!" I said with a sudden burst of courage I didn't think I was capable of. But saying it and doing it were two very different things. It took all the will I could muster to actually move my feet... but I did. But, after several steps I glanced back, only to discover that Win wasn't behind me.

"Win, what's wrong?" I called back to him.

Win just stared at me, terror etched on his face. "I can't do it, man," he said. "I'm terrified of heights!"

"Win, it's totally safe!" I called, beckoning him to come.

"Look!" I said, jumping up and down several times on the sky bridge to show him it was secure. "See?"

It was no use. The man I had just watched smash through a wall with nothing but strength and determination was now unable to move his feet.

"You go!" he called out. "I'll stay here and guard the stairwell until you get back."

There was nothing else I could do. I nodded, turned, and started across the sky bridge that led to *Courage Crafters*, the place that no one at The Fear Factory wanted to talk about.

Chapter Sixteen: Courage Crafters

As I descended the stairs on the other end of the sky bridge I felt my throat go dry, but I realized it wasn't from fear or nervousness; it was from dust. The place was a mess, cobwebs stretching across open doorways. Apparently no one had come through here in years.

I ducked my head into an open office door to find it was empty. Then another, and another. It looked was as if the building were abandoned. Then I heard voices coming from down the hall. I turned the corner and entered what looked like a small break room where a man and woman stood, chatting. They jumped when they saw me.

"Jeez, you scared us!" the man gasped. "Who are you? How did you get in here?"

"My name is Steven Traynor, I came over the sky bridge…"

"You crossed the sky bridge!?!" the woman said, looking positively amazed.

"That's not possible!" the man declared. "The sky bridge is sealed off!"

"Not anymore," I said. "Is that a problem?"

"A problem? No, it's just… well, that…" The man's words trailed off and he looked to the woman for help.

"What Bill is trying to say is that we've gotten used to things being… well, being the way they are," the woman said.

"And how exactly are things?" I asked.

"Quiet. Very, very quiet."

"So, what exactly do you want?" the man named Bill asked.

"Want? Well, I don't know!" I said. "I just got tired of The Fear Factory's constant B.S. and I was hoping that …"

"That, what? That we could sell you some courage?"

"Yes! I guess so!"

The pair broke into uproarious laughter. When they'd composed themselves, the woman led me down a hallway to a door with a nameplate that read: *M. Smith, CCO.* Then she led me into the small, sparsely-decorated office.

"CCO?" I inquired.

"Chief Courage Officer," the woman said, "but no need for formalities - feel free to call me Maggie."

Maggie sat down in a cheap, black vinyl chair behind an old metal desk. "As you can tell, we don't quite have the budget they've got over at The Fear Factory. Coffee?"

"No, thanks. What I'd like is to know why those guys can sell fear to people all day long, but you can't sell me courage?"

"Why? Because it just doesn't work that way."

I lowered myself in an orange plastic chair across from her.

"Okay," I said, exhaling in frustration; "How *does* it work?"

Maggie shifted in her chair; put her elbows on the desk. "When you're born you start with…"

"…I know, I know, three standard fears," I said, cutting her off and finishing her sentence. Remember, I just came from The Fear Factory."

"Anyway, all other fears are acquired over time," Maggie continued, not skipping a beat. "But courage is different. When you're born, courage simply comes standard with the package."

"You mean that…?"

"I mean that there's no reason for *Courage Crafters* to have a sales force, or to sell courage to people, because every person on the planet already has all the inner strength and courage they'll ever need… inside them already… at birth!"

"Is this really true?" I asked in disbelief.

"Of course it is! Do you have kids?" she asked.

I shook my head, no.

"Then think back to when *you* were a kid. Remember what you went through to learn to ride a bike?"

"Sure," I said.

"Did you fall off at all while trying to get it? Scrape any knees or elbows?"

"Yeah, a lot!"

"That's because you had the desire to learn, and the courage to do whatever it took to achieve your goal, it was already there. No one had to put it there."

"Yeah, but I remember my father out there, cheering me on. He was giving me courage, wasn't he?"

"No. By cheering you on your father wasn't giving you courage, he was helping you tap into the courage that was already inside you. Instead of Courage Crafters I guess you could call us *Courage Incorporated,* because - in reality - courage is automatically *incorporated* into each human being who ever lived, right at birth! What I'm trying to tell you, Steven, is that no human being can give courage to another person, nor do they need to. Each of us has all the courage we'll ever need... inside us already."

"So then why do I feel so un-courageous?"

"As we get older, Steven, we acquire more and more fears, to the point where our fears outweigh our courage. Think of it as a scale..." Maggie said, rising from her desk.

She walked to a large white board and started drawing on it with a dry erase marker. "When we're born, the scale is tipped entirely in favor of courage. That's why we think we can do virtually anything, including flying to the moon by simply flapping our arms.

But, over time - once The Fear Factory starts getting into the act - the scale starts to tip in the other direction. At first we hardly notice, but then, one day, the scale suddenly tips in the opposite direction and we start wondering: *Where did our courage go?*

The answer, of course, is that it didn't go anywhere. It's simply buried by the shear amount of fears we've accumulated and is no longer easily accessible."

I sat there, stunned speechless. All the courage I would ever need was inside me already? This was something I'd never considered.

"There is no getting around it," she continued. "Either you conquer your fear or it will conquer you. But, like the cowardly lion in the *Wizard of Oz*, the courage he wanted so desperately was in him the whole time. Now, that said... *there is a handbook."*

"What? There's a handbook? That makes no sense. If all the courage we need is already in us, why on Earth would we need a handbook?"

Maggie stood, then walked to a wall safe and carefully began turning the dial.

"Just because the courage is inside us, that doesn't mean people don't need help accessing it," she said as she withdrew a bound manual from the safe and placed it on the metal desk in front of me. I picked up the manual and looked at the cover. There were no words, just an embossed lion's head.

"A lion?" I asked.

"Yes. The universal symbol for courage."

I opened the book and looked at the first page which read: *The Courage Crafters Handbook: A guide for overcoming self-imposed limitations and rediscovering your inner strength.* I began flipping through the pages. It was amazing.

"I'd like to buy a copy," I blurted.

"Sorry, your money is no good here, Mr. Traynor."

"That's very kind of you," I replied, picking up the manual and standing to leave.

"No, you don't understand," Maggie said. "I'm not giving you the handbook, Mr. Traynor. I mean the handbook - it's not for sale."

"What do you mean, it's not for sale? You tease me with the solution to my problems, then tell me I can't have it?"

"That's the problem, Mr. Traynor. The manual you're holding isn't a copy... *it's the original.* That's why we keep it locked in the safe! But you're invited to sit here and read through it, if you'd like. After all, you've got..."

"Let me guess... *all the time in the world?*"

And with that, Maggie Smith winked and walked out of the office, closing the door behind her, leaving me to study what I knew might be the most important book ever written.

Chapter Seventeen: The Courage Crafters Handbook

I spent what seemed like hours reading *The Courage Crafters Handbook,* fascinated at the many things I didn't know, should have learned earlier, but mostly did know at one time or another, but had simply forgotten. The book began with a section dedicated to quotes from past members of the *Courage Crafters Board of Directors:*

> *He who loses wealth loses much. He who loses a friend loses more. But he who loses courage loses all.*
> -Cervantes

> *Life shrinks or expands in proportion to one's courage.*
> -Anise Nan

> *Everyone has talent. What is rare is the courage to follow that talent to the dark place where it leads.*
> -Erica Jong

> *Courage is resistance to fear, mastery of fear, not absence of fear.*
> -Mark Twain

> *It's a sad day when you find out that it's not an accident or time or fortune, but just yourself that kept things from you.*
> -Lillian Hellman

> *Go confidently in the direction of your dreams! Live the life you've imagined.*
> - Henry David Thoreau

All dreams can come true – if we have the courage to pursue them.
-Walt Disney

Courage is being scared to death, and saddling up anyway.
-John Wayne

I never take counsel of my fears. I've never even been visited by a Fear Factory rep – they're probably scared to death of me!
-George Patton

Next, there were a number of chapters, each dedicated to specific ways and techniques for accessing the courage that was already inside us. I flipped to the chapter on desensitizing yourself to the things you fear and read:

...the only way to desensitize yourself to the thing you fear is to do the thing you fear. Avoidance will never work. Hiding in a darkened room only makes the problem worse, because fear grows like bacteria in the darkness. When you hide from your fears, you create an endless loop of fear that grows and feeds on itself.

Then I turned to a section called taking action to reclaim your life and read:

...the only antidote to fear is action. You can't wish fear away; you can only do it away. Do something every day that scares you! Do the thing, you shall have the power! Or, in the words of our esteemed past board member, Abraham Maslow: "One can choose to go back toward safety or forward toward growth. Growth must be chosen again and again; fear must be overcome again and again."

Finally, I turned to the chapter titled turning fear into fuel and read:

...the biggest problem we have is in the way we think of fear in the first place. We see it as our enemy, something we need to banish. No! Fear is to be embraced! Imagine, for example, that one gets nervous every time they are asked to give a speech. What if, just before the speech, you were given the energy to give the greatest presentation of your life? Well, you are. It's called fear! The only difference between fear and energy is the way you decide to label it.

It was as if the handbook was speaking directly to me. Then, at the bottom of the last page, the handbook stated:

...there's one last thing you need to know in order to conquer your fear and lead the life you've always wanted... perhaps the most important secret of all, which is...

I quickly turned the page, eager to discover the secret - but there was no final page. The final page was missing.

At that moment the door opened and Maggie Smith entered. "Where's the last page?" I demanded.

"Oh, that. The Fear Factory stole it."

"They stole it? What do you mean, they stole it?"

"Happened years ago. I think it scared them, which is funny if you think about it, something scaring The Fear Factory," she said.

"Well, what did it say? The last page, what was on it?" I asked, frantic.

"Jeez," Maggie managed, thinking, "it's been so long now that no one really remembers. But…"

"But what?"

"Well, rumor has it that they keep the last page, the one they stole, in a secret room somewhere over there, locked up tight."

"Where is this room? I need to find it."

"I have no idea. But someone did say something once about a red door… HEY, WAIT!" she called out. "Wait! Wait! The handbook! You can't take the handbook!"

But Maggie's words were barely audible as I dashed out of the office and up the hallway, the Courage Crafters Handbook tucked under my arm like big Win Clark carrying a football, on my way back to The Fear Factory.

Chapter Eighteen: Back to The Fear Factory

When I reached the bottom of the stairs on the opposite side of the sky bridge I was surprised to find that Win was nowhere in sight. "So much for guarding the stairway," I mumbled to myself, climbing back through the ragged hole. I worked my way back into the main corridor of The Fear Factory in the direction of Sturgess' office where the red door awaited. And I was almost there when two uniformed guards appeared and began walking directly toward me.

"They're not looking for you," I said to myself as one of the guards spoke into a handheld walkie-talkie. Seconds later a loud siren whirred to life and lights began to flash along the ceiling. Apparently I was wrong.

So I did the only thing I could think to do. *I ran.*

Before the guards could react I flew past them, racing down the hall as fast as my legs could carry me, the guards close on my heels. I turned the corner and saw two people still in their costumes from the party, one dressed as a computer and the other as a giant squid. I sure hope these costumes are padded, I thought as I grabbed the computer by the keyboard and pulled it to the ground, then yanking the six-foot calamari by its tentacles and toppling it on the crashed computer.

And while this didn't stop the guards entirely, it bought me several precious seconds to secret myself under a stairwell. Moments later the guards ran past and the coast was clear, at least for the time being.

It was then that I realized the awful truth: *Big Win Clark, my hero, had sold me out.*

Chapter Nineteen: Caught in the Act

I made my way past the main auditorium and down the hall until eventually it grew pitch black, just like the previous time. Placing my hands on the wall I felt my way once more to Sturgess' office door and was relieved to find it still unlocked.

As I closed the door behind me I found an unpleasant surprise waiting. Standing in the office were the same two guards I had encountered earlier. The first guard raised his walkie-talkie to his mouth: "We've got him."

Several seconds later the walkie-talkie crackled and a voice said, "Sit tight, the Head Fear Master will be right down."

I found myself sitting in Sturgess' chair for the third time now, however this time there would be no going into the computer or anywhere else for that matter, as the guards handcuffed my wrists tightly behind my back. After what seemed like forever the door opened and Miles Sturgess entered the office, followed closely by Allison.

"I don't think handcuffs are necessary," Sturgess said to the guard nearest him. "Are they, Steven?"

"No, I'll be a good boy," I said sarcastically as the cuffs were removed.

As I rubbed my wrists to regain circulation, Allison approached, placing her hand on my shoulder.

"I'm so sorry about this. I was just trying to protect you, I swear. I had no other choice but to call them." Her words hit me like a punch in the solar plexus. Win hadn't sold me out at all. It had been Allison.

"Well, at least you overcame your fear of the phone," I said sarcastically. Tears quickly welled up in Allison's eyes, and she turned and ran from the office. Then Sturgess motioned for the guards to leave.

"I thought the Head Fear Master was coming down," I said curtly. "Apparently I don't rate very high on the threat scale."

Sturgess shook his head. "Don't worry, he knows you're here."

"Good, because I've got a thing or two to tell him!" I barked.

"Really?" Sturgess replied with a sense of amusement. "Like what?"

"I'm going to tell him how I'm going to close this place down, how I'm going to turn off the lights, lock the doors and shutter this place forever. I'm going to burn this place to the ground!"

"Interesting," said Sturgess, studying me. "And how, exactly, are you going to do all this?"

"I haven't figured that out yet," I admitted. "But when I do, watch out."

"You act as though existence of The Fear Factory is a bad thing, Steven, as if the world would be a better place without it."

"It would be!" I barked loudly.

"Now, that's where you're wrong, Steven. Very wrong. As the venerable Mark Twain once said, *'Courage is resistance to and mastery of fear...'*"

"...not the absence of it," I said, finishing the quote. "I know, it's in the handbook."

Sturgess glanced at the Courage Crafters Handbook over on the desk, where the guards had placed it. "Well, the question, Steven, is - if courage is the resistance and mastery of fear, then how can one ever be courageous without the *existence* of fear? Don't you see? According to this handbook you treasure so much, that fear is a necessity? Fear is a protector, designed to keep you safe. And it can be a motivator, as well. Plus - if you don't mind me taking the truth about fear all the way - fear is actually part of what makes life worth living!"

I couldn't believe my ears. Fear helped make life worth living? Was he out of his mind? "You're so deep into this fear thing, Sturgess, you've lost all perspective."

"No, Steven, it's *you* who has lost all perspective," the old man said, leaning his aging frame against his desk. "Can't you see that the fears you have inside you are a gift?"

"A gift? You have got to be kidding me." I laughed.

"No, Steven. When it comes to fear, I'm as serious as a heart attack. Imagine a world without fear and ask yourself: *Is it a truly better world?*"

"Hell, yes!" I responded.

"Well, if you think that, then you're not thinking! You truly believe a world without challenges and obstacles would be a better world to live in? Sure, there'd be less pain, sorrow and angst, but there'd also be less joy and satisfaction and triumph. Fear provides balance to the world, Steven. It provides the mountains we climb. It provides the hurdles we jump. Fear is the defense that your friend and idol 'Big Win' Clark must strategize, struggle and toil against to score the winning touchdown! In the final days, as your life is drawing to a close, what do you think you're going to reminisce about, the stuff that came easy? Or the hard-fought victories? What do you think you'll remember most, Steven - the $100 bill you accidently found in the gutter? Or the prospect you called on for years who finally bought from you?"

I had to admit, Sturgess had captured my attention. And he wasn't finished:

"Bad people, like terrorists, use fear as a tool to rob people of their humanity and their lives, I understand that.

But a hammer can be used to build a building, or to knock one down. The problem is not the tool, Steven - it's how the tool is used. Fear can just as easily provide the energy to succeed as to zap one's energy and lead to failure. When it comes to life, the problem is not your fear - it's what you do with it."

Could he be right? I wondered. Could I have had it wrong all this time? Could fear be part of what makes life worth living?

"So, is there anything else you'd like to tell the Head Fear Master, if he were here?" Sturgess asked.

"No, that's pretty much it," I said, my breathing still heavy with anger.

"Well, then, consider the message delivered," Sturgess said.

Chapter Twenty: The Head Fear Master

"You're the Head Fear Master?" I stammered in disbelief. *"You run this place?"*

"Well, these days I leave the day-to-day operations to others. But I do keep myself busy creating a new fear every now and then," the old man said with a sly smile, pulling himself out of his chair and to his feet.

"Remember the tour?" Sturgess asked.

"Yeah, loads of fun," I said. "Like Disneyland, but without the lines."

"They share the top ten fears," he continued, ignoring my sarcasm, "but they don't actually share the *real* number one fear."

"Yeah? What's that?"

"It's the one that's too painful for us to face; the fear that we are simply not enough. It's not the things that come our way that we fear, it's that we won't be able to handle them - *that's the real fear we all grapple with most.* But you know what's interesting?"

"I'm sure you're going to tell me."

"The solution to being enough comes down to one simple thing; *taking action.* And it doesn't matter if the action you take is right or wrong, successful or unsuccessful - *it only matters that you do something.* Anything.

Because when you don't take action, it's like adding a brick to the wall that serves as the barrier between you and your destiny. But when you *do* take action, it's like removing a brick from that very same wall.

"Most people refuse to take action," Sturgess continued, "because they're afraid it won't be enough… that they'll come up short. And to find out we're not as good as we hoped is horribly frightening. But you know what? None of us are as good as we hope! But we're also never as bad as we feared! The irony, of course, is that if you don't take action to overcome your fears, your fears come true! But if you do take action, even if everything you attempt is unsuccessful, your life most assuredly will matter. Because there is but one primary purpose to life - just one - and do you know what it is?"

I couldn't believe my ears. The man who makes his living frightening people was going to tell me the purpose of life.

"This should be entertaining," I said sarcastically.

"The purpose of life," said Sturgess in a steady, serious voice, is… *growth*. What matters most in life is that we grow, in some way, every single day. To move toward our potential. To get up every day and to come to the edge of our abilities, to see if we can be just a little better, learn just a little more.

And you know what, Steven? People who do that have a greater sense of happiness and contentment than you can imagine.

The goal of our actions should not be luxury - no, the goal of our actions should be victory. More specifically, victory over our own limitations, not victory over others. Winning over others is easy; all you have to do is compete with others who have less drive or ability than you. But winning against yourself... ah, that takes some doing. *That... takes... courage!"*

'And courage requires fear to exist,' I thought to myself. He was right.

Chapter Twenty-One: The Final Page

My encounter with Sturgess had proven to be overwhelming, and I found myself trying hard to wrap my brain around everything he had said.   But there was still one other thing I wanted to know.

"So, what's behind the red door?" I asked.

"Behind the door?" Sturgess said.

"Yes, and don't B.S. me!" I said.

"You act like you know, so you tell me, Steven."

"It's the secret on the final page of the Courage Crafters Handbook," I said, raising the bound manual up in my hand. "And I want to see it. Now!"

"That's what you came back here for," Sturgess asked, "to learn the secret to overcoming your fears and leading the life of your dreams?"
Yes, I nodded.

"You sure you want to know? After all, the truth can be very painful sometimes."

"Open the door," I said.

"Very well,"   the old man said, pulling a set of keys from his pocket and walking over to the red door.   Sturgess inserted a key in the lock… turned it… opened the door and stepped to the side.

Without saying a word I walked past him and straight into the room and looked around. The room was completely... *empty*.

"They lied to me," I said.

"Have they?" Sturgess asked.

"Yes, there's nothing in here!"

"Really? Look again, Steven, and this time, look carefully," he said.

I scanned the room with my eyes and noticed a mirror on the back wall. I walked over and looked into it. "I don't understand," I said, staring at my reflection.

"The room was empty before you entered, but now that you've entered it, the answer to the final page *is* in the room."

"I don't understand," I said once again - but I understood fully. Sturgess was right – the truth can be very painful.

"Don't you see, Steven," Sturgess said with a knowing smile. "The Fear Factory... is... you."

Chapter Twenty-Two: It's All You

"For a bright guy, you're a slow learner," Sturgess stated flatly. Then - as if he were made of some sort of plasma - Sturgess' body began to shape-shift, morphing somehow. And an instant later Sturgess was no longer Sturgess. Suddenly he was... *Win!*

"Win?" I managed.

"Yeah, it's me, your buddy, Win. What did you learn from me, Steven?"

"I learned that everyone has fears," I stammered, "even people you'd never think could be afraid of anything."

"Good," said the Win-figure standing before me. Then Win's body began to morph as well, suddenly becoming Maggie Smith from *Courage Crafters*.

"And what did you learn from me?" Maggie asked.

"I learned that all the courage I will ever need is already inside me," I said. Maggie Smith smiled, then began to morph as well, and a moment later I was face to face with the most beautiful woman I had ever seen. Allison.

"And what did you learn from me, Steven?" Allison asked.

"I learned that if you don't fight your fears with everything you have, you can become so comfortable with them that they become your entire world."

Then Allison began to morph into someone else. Who would be the next? I wondered. Finally, I found myself standing face to face with the last person I expected to encounter...

Me.

"And what did you learn from me?" the other version of myself asked.

"I learned that I want more from life, from myself, and that I'm done playing it safe," I said, glancing at the Courage Crafters handbook over on the table. "And I learned that I have the ability to push past my fears and become the courageous person I was always meant to be."

Then the *me-image* looked me straight in the eyes, filling me with the understanding that it really was... *true!* All the courage I could ever want or need was, indeed, already inside me - and that no one could ever take it away without my consent.

Then the image morphed back into the form of Sturgess.

I said: "So this place, the people, all of it... is..."

"Your creation, Steven," Sturgess said. "All of it. It's been you all along."

"But why now? Why today?" I asked.

"Maybe it's like you said; maybe you were just sick and tired of being sick and tired. Maybe it was that buffoon Doug Appleton pushing your buttons. Who knows?

The important thing is that you now understand that fear is a reflexive emotion, one that can be harnessed and governed.

Humans will always live with fear, and that's okay. But living in fear? That is a choice."

And right then, for the first time in years I felt completely... whole.

"Thank you," was all I could manage to say.

"No need. I've done nothing, because it's been you all along," said Miles Sturgess, the Head Fear Master in my mind. Then the curious little man took a step toward me, wrapped his spindly, frail arms around me and gave me a hug, and whispered in my ear: *"In the future, should we ever meet again - and we will - just tell me to go away. I'll understand."*

Chapter Twenty-Three: Leaving the Fear Factory Behind

"So, since I apparently own this place, I guess I'm free to go," I said with a smile.

"True! But it seems you're forgetting something, don't you think?" Sturgess said, pointing his finger at the now open door.

"I don't understand..." I started to say. But suddenly I understood completely.

Allison.

"If I'm not mistaken," Sturgess said, "there's another tour starting in just a few minutes."

I rushed from the room and down to hall to find Allison standing before a whole new group of fear factory tourists. "Good morning, everyone. Welcome to The Fear Factory! My name is Allison and..."

She saw me approaching, stopped mid-sentence as I worked my way through the crowd and grabbed her by the hand.

"Come on, we're going!" I said, pulling her along.

"Wait! I can't just leave, I've got a tour..." I spun around, faced her. "These people? They don't exist, Allison. They're not real."

"Of course they're real!" she protested. I could hear both disbelief and fear in Allison's voice. I was going to have to do something dramatic to convince her.

"No, they're not," I said, turning and facing a man in a black double-breasted suit.

"See this guy? Watch." I leveled a stare at the man, hoping that what I was going to try would work. "I made you appear here," I said to the man, "and I can make you disappear."

And suddenly... just like that... the man began to dissipate, particle by particle, to the horrified gasps of the others in the group, until he was simply no longer there.

I turned back to Allison. "See? These people don't exist. This entire place, it doesn't exist. It's all an illusion, Allison. It's not real! The Fear Factory is nothing more than an illusion of our own making."

"But... but this can't be! It can't!" she cried. "I'm real! I'm real!" Tears welled up in Allison's eyes and she looked at me, terrified. And it was at that moment that I realized the final truth; *if everything and everyone here was of my own making, simply all an illusion, then Allison was an illusion, too.*

So why was I trying so hard to make her come along? To rescue her?

It's hard to explain, but I suddenly realized who Allison really was - she was the part of me that liked this place - the part of me that felt comfortable here.   And saving Allison wasn't about saving Allison at all... it was the final step in saving myself.

"You're coming," I said, pulling her by the wrist to the elevator and pushing the down button.

"Have you lost your mind?" she screamed.

"No, Allison, just the opposite. I've finally gotten control of it!" The elevator doors slid open. "Get in. Trust me!" And despite her fear... *my fear*... Allison stepped into the elevator and the doors slid closed behind us.

The elevator began its rapid descent, but suddenly jolted to an abrupt stop - the lights going out as we were thrown into total darkness.

"What's happening?" she yelled. "Oh my God!"

Then, the elevator reversed direction and started to climb... slowly at first... then faster and faster and faster. "Here, take my hand," I said to her. "Take my hand... take my hand... take my hand..."

Chapter Twenty-Four: Home Again

"Here, take my hand," I heard a male voice say. I opened my eyes and found Doug Appleton standing over me.

"Let me help you up," Appleton said, grabbing my hand and pulling me to my feet.

"Where's Allison?" I asked as Doug led me from the elevator.

"Allison? Allison who?"

"The tour guide," I said, glancing around the 14th floor hallway of Fearn international's headquarters.

"Man, you're delirious. Good thing I'm here. You fainted, Steve, totally passed out on me."

"What? How long have I been out?" I said in disbelief. "I don't know, about 30 seconds," Doug replied. I glanced at my watch which read: 9:55 a.m. Only *one minute* had passed.

"We were talking about the presentation and blam! You went down like a sack of potatoes! At least the last time you made it into the room before doing a header," Doug said with a chuckle. "We'd better get a move on, I've got a presentation to make."

And that was the moment the final tumbler fell into place. I had had enough.

Enough of being afraid.

Enough of performing below my potential.

Enough wishing but not acting.

Enough.

Enough.

Enough.

It took Doug a moment to notice that I had stopped walking. He turned around, looked back. "You coming?" Doug asked. "You know, if you want you can just sit out here in the hall."

"I have a better idea, Dougie," I said, reaching out and taking the projector case from his hand. "How about you stay in the hall, and I'll make the presentation on my own."

"Seriously, Steve..." Doug started.

"No, seriously Doug - take a seat right over there," I said, pointing to a chair in the waiting area. "If for any reason I need you, I'll send up a flare."

Doug studied my eyes for several long seconds and i could tell that something had changed.

"Yeah, sure Steve. You're the boss, anything you say." And with that I turned around and headed up the hall.

Epilogue: One Year Later

A year has passed since my visit to The Fear Factory, and I can look back now and realize what an amazing thing happened to me that day.

Often people talk about the day that changed their life. When they do, it's usually the result of something like surviving a car crash or meeting their soul mate. The day I stumbled into The Fear Factory, whether real or imagined, was that day for me. Because it was the day I came face to face with my greatest enemy, and came away with the realization that sometimes the only thing standing between us and happiness and freedom and success is... *ourselves.*

I recall looking back over my shoulder as I walked through the large glass doors that led to Fearn International's corporate suite and seeing Doug standing there, his face filled with confusion, as if he were looking at someone he'd never seen before. That, of course, was because the person he climbed into the elevator with was not the same person who stepped off.

Several days after returning from the presentation Doug gave his two-week notice, citing a lack of opportunity for growth at our firm as his reason for leaving. Yvonne wanted to know if I had had anything to do with Doug's decision. I just shrugged.

Since that day my sales numbers at Ramsden+Media have exploded, due in large part to an increased number of speaking engagements on my part. Some people call them sales calls, but to me they will always be more. Because each and every one of them represents an opportunity for growth, a chance for me to stretch myself, even if it's for an audience of one.

You may be wondering how the presentation went. It went well. Not perfect - but pretty darn well. But perfection is no longer the yardstick by which I judge myself. Now I judge myself on growth. And every day, I simply ask: *Did you challenge yourself today? Did you grow? Are you better than you were yesterday?*

Any day the answers come back 'yes' I consider to be a win.

Everyone tells me I've changed. Even Yvonne. When I got back to Seattle after the presentation she called me into her office and told me that the CEO of Fearn International had called with the news: We didn't get the deal. But he also said that I had 'wowed' them. And that, Yvonne said, was all she could ask.

The truth is, I haven't changed. I've simply become me again - the person I was always supposed to be.

And just last week an amazing thing happened; Fearn International called, saying they were unhappy with the firm they'd gone with. They asked Yvonne if she could send Steven Traynor back to chat. Not just someone from the firm - they wanted me.

And, I admit I would probably be more excited about it, but my attention has been elsewhere. Because tonight I have a date... *with Allison*. Not Allison, really - her name is Benita, but she bears a striking resemblance to Allison and is every bit as wonderful, smart and stunning. We met when I was trying out a new coffee shop one morning. And you'll never guess what she does for a living: She's in telemarketing!

So, today I'm taking off a bit early to drop by Nordstrom and buy myself a new tie for our date.

I'm thinking red.

* * * * * * *

Sneak Peak of GO FOR NO!

A #1 Amazon Sales & Selling book
by Richard Fenton & Andrea Waltz

We pulled up to valet parking at Rainwater's on Kettner, a well-known restaurant near San Diego's Gaslamp District, which I had always wanted to eat at but never had the opportunity or the means. After we were seated Eric chose a nice bottle of Stag's Leap Cabernet which we sipped while waiting for our steaks to arrive.

"I read our book today," I started with a laugh, eager to explore the mystery of my being there.

"Oh yeah, which one?"

"Fail Your Way to Success," I responded.

"And what did you think?"

"Honestly? I liked it."

He smiled and looked truly pleased as the waiter placed our steaks in front of us.

"Did you discover any clues, anything that might explain why this is happening?"

"Perhaps. From what I can tell, virtually everything in our lives has been identical. We were both born on the same day to the same parents, and we each have an older brother named Carl. We grew up in the same neighborhood, went to the same schools and had the same teachers. We worked the same jobs during high school and we both sold suits at Dubin's Clothing for Men during college. But then something happened…"

"What do you mean, something happened?" he asked.

"All the experiences you wrote about in your book were identical to mine, that is, right up until the job at the clothing store," I responded. "It's at that point that things changed somehow."

"What changed?"

"Well, in the book you mentioned an encounter you had with the district manager, a guy named Harold. Do you remember?"

"Do I remember? How could I forget? That's the day that changed my life!" he exclaimed.

"That's the problem. That day never happened to me."

"What do you mean? How can a day not happen?"

"Of course that day happened, it just didn't happen the same way for me as it did for you."

"You mean to say you don't remember the conversation with Harold that day?" he asked incredulously.

"Honestly, I couldn't begin to tell you a single thing Harold said," I replied.

"Wow! Then maybe that's where we need to start!"

*   *   *

"I remember it like it was yesterday," the other Eric began. "I, or we, had only been working at Dubin's for about a month when the district manager, Harold, was scheduled to do a store visit and I really wanted to impress him. As you may remember we weren't doing very well sales-wise," he recounted, "and quite honestly I was worried that if my personal sales didn't improve that they were going to let me go. This is right after Elaine and I got married, and the last thing I needed was to suddenly be without a job."

"I remember it well," I said in agreement.

"Harold showed up about nine-thirty in the morning and everybody said their hellos, coffee and donuts and all that, and at ten o'clock we opened the doors. I was the first salesman in that morning so I had first ups. Sound familiar so far?"

I nodded.

"Then," he continued, "in walks this finely-dressed gentleman who announces that he wants to buy an entire wardrobe of clothing! And, within thirty minutes, I have my biggest sale ever. I was certain that Harold would be impressed."

"I remember that too," I said.

"After the customer left, Harold finally sauntered over and said, 'Nice sale kid.' My chest puffed out with pride. 'Eleven hundred dollars!' I proclaimed. But Harold just stood there and didn't seem overly impressed. Finally he said, 'I'm just curious, but what did that customer say no to?' 'What do you mean?' I shot back. 'That guy just bought a suit, sport coat, three shirts, six ties, shoes, socks, a belt and underwear! What do you mean, what did he say no to?'

"Harold waited calmly for me to stop being defensive, then he said, 'We've already established what he said yes to. What I want to know now is, what did he say no to?'

"I thought for a long time, mentally reviewing the sale in my mind, then sheepishly I replied, 'Nothing. That customer didn't say no to anything.' 'So,' Harold asked, 'then how did you know he was done?'

"His question hit me like a punch because I suddenly realized the customer hadn't ended the sale, I had! Why? For only one reason I could think of... the customer had hit my mental spending limit. I realized that I had never spent over a thousand bucks on a shopping trip ever, so when anyone went over my mental spending limit, hey... they were done!"

"I pretty much remember that," I said, "but it didn't have that much impact on me. That's what changed your life?"

"Yes. That and what Harold said next. He said, 'The salesperson never decides when the sale is over, the customer does.' Then he looked me in the eye and said, 'Eric, your fear of hearing the word 'no' is the only thing standing between you and greatness.'

"It was amazing. I had gone into work that morning hoping to keep my job, and I went home that night just two letters away from greatness."

Two letters from greatness, I heard myself repeating. N and O. No.

* * *

To learn more about Go for No! and to order a copy of the best-selling book, visit wwwGoforNo.com

About the Authors...

Richard Fenton & Andrea Waltz are the founders of Courage Crafters, a business dedicated to helping others achieve breakthrough performance. "The ultimate challenge in life," says the pair, "is not in beating others, but rather, overcoming your own imaginary limitations. If you can just get out of your own way, the road to success is often a clear path." They speak together internationally on how to achieve extraordinary success by learning to fail more often. Their articles have been published in hundreds of online and offline journals, including several times in SUCCESS MAGAZINE.

Richard and Andrea have written 4 books but 'Go for No!' is the most popular closing in on 300,000 copies sold. It has been on #1 on Amazon's 'Sales & Selling' Best Seller list and remains in the top 20 after the last three years.

For information on having Rich and Andrea speak to your group, call **800-290-5028** or visit them at **www.couragecrafters.com.**

We hope you enjoyed reading *The Fear Factory!*

The Fear Factory

Sometimes the Only Thing Standing Between You and Success is… You!

Milton Keynes UK
Ingram Content Group UK Ltd.
UKHW020020011223
433475UK00009B/149